The Camel and the Evil People

by
Saniyasnain Khan

Goodwordkidz

One of the Prophets sent to mankind in northern Arabia after the Great Flood was Salih ﷺ. He was born into the Thamud tribe. This tribe was known for the beautiful houses that they carved out of the mountainsides.

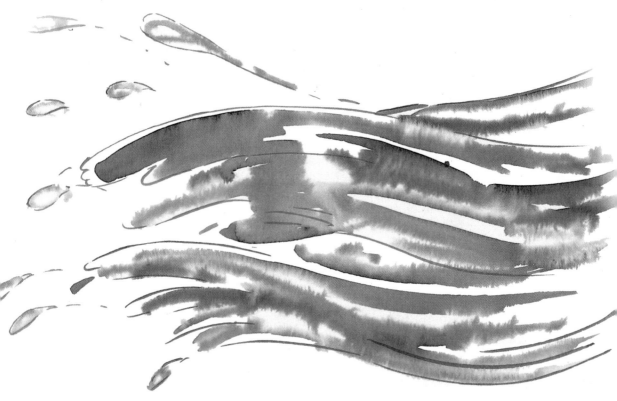

The Prophet Salih عَلَيْهِ السَّلَام was unhappy to see that his people liked worshipping idols. He asked them to pray to Allah alone and reminded them that He had made them the heirs of Ad, and given them houses to live in.

"You have built mansions on its plains and hew out houses from the mountains. Remember Allah's favor and do not make the earth a wicked place." Salih ﷺلسّلام continued, "Will you not fear Allah? I am indeed your true messenger."

"...are you to be left secure in this land, amidst gardens and fountains, cornfields and palm trees laden with fine fruit, hewing your dwellings out of the mountains and leading a wicked life? Fear Allah and follow me."

But the haughty elders of the people of Thamud were heartless and said there was no such thing as the Day of Judgement. They said, "Are we to follow a mortal who stands alone among us? That would surely be wrong and mad. Did he alone among us receive this warning? He is indeed a foolish liar!"

They could not think of giving up the religion of their forefathers. They even said Salih ﷺ and his followers would do wicked things and taunted the weak about their belief in him. Finally, they were put to the test by means of a she-camel. Salih ﷺ said, "This is Allah's own she-camel (*naqat allah*), a sign for you."

Leave her to graze at will on Allah's own land, and do not harm her, lest you are instantly punished." They were also told to give a full share of water to the she-camel along with their own herds and flocks. But, feeling very angry at this, they called their most wicked tribesman, Qudar ibn Salif, who hamstrung the she-camel, then killed her.

After having done such a bad thing, the people of Thamud haughtily challenged Salih: "Now bring down the punishment you threaten us with, if you truly are a messenger." Salih عليه السلام told them that they had only three days to live in their houses, as this was Allah's will.

Even then, instead of feeling sorry, they plotted to kill Salih ﷺ and his family. Nine tribesmen, while taking an oath to carry out their sinful act, said to each other: "We will say to his kinsmen: 'We were not even present when they were slain. What we say is the truth.'"

But, before they could carry out their evil plot, Allah punished them with terrible earthquake.

When Allah did so, He saved Salih علیه السلام and his followers, while a dreadful cry rang out above the evil-doers.

When morning came, they were lying dead in their dwellings, as though they had never had a good life there.